HABIT-B

HABIT-BUSTING

stop smoking

PETE COHEN

Foreword by Dr Hilary Jones

element

Element
An Imprint of HarperCollins*Publishers*
77–85 Fulham Palace Road
Hammersmith, London W6 8JB

The website address is:
www.thorsonselement.com

and *Element* are trademarks of
HarperCollins*Publishers* Limited

Published by Element 2003

10 9 8 7 6 5 4 3 2 1

A catalogue record of this book
is available from the British Library

ISBN 0 00 715496 8

Printed and bound in Great Britain by
Martins The Printers Limited, Berwick upon Tweed

Contents

Foreword

Giving up smoking is the single most important step anyone can make towards future good health and freedom from disease. Don't even think about arguing with me. Smoking has horrible consequences. Smoking is evil. Not least because it's such a pleasurable pastime until it kills you.

You might be toying with the idea of quitting right now – vaguely conscious of the fact that you are not as well as you could be, and increasingly aware on a day-by-day basis of your own mortality. But you haven't had to break the bad news, as I have so often, to someone who always thought they'd get away with a lifetime's smoking only to develop lung cancer at a relatively young age and end their days with increasing shortness of breath and acute suffocation. It really isn't worth it.

But HOW does a smoker stop smoking? When someone is really very badly hooked on the habit, distant fears of possible ill health hardly matter. Doctors' advice is easy to ignore. Friends and family condone your addiction, loathe to deprive you of a craving they know you cannot resist. It's easier to let you die.

That's where Pete Cohen comes in. The guy who can give you back your life. I've known Pete for years, and his mind-altering approach coupled with his unwavering enthusiasm never ceases to amaze me. He makes the uncomfortable and unwelcome task of habit-busting a fascinating, rewarding and very effective pleasure. His techniques are ground-breaking and inspirational, but, most importantly, they work. This book can stop you smoking. Read it now to stop smoking immediately. Then read it again to avoid any complacency. And enjoy.

Dr Hilary Jones, M.B.B.S.
GP and media doctor

Introduction

Dear Habit Buster,

My name is Pete Cohen and I would like to welcome you to *Habit-Busting: Stop Smoking*.

I have always found human behaviour fascinating, and through my explorations and experiences of working with thousands of people I am convinced that the majority of people can break any unwanted bad habits. Habits are quite simply things we have learned, whether it's smoking, low self-esteem, nail-biting or procrastinating. They are thoughts, behaviours and actions that we have practised over time.

Like many of the other essential skills we learn as we grow, such as talking, eating and walking, habits are behaviours we learn by watching others and copying them. We do this because these habits appear to make others look and/or feel good. Our motivation to learn is no different: we believe we are smoking/biting our nails/procrastinating in our own best interests – to make ourselves happy. So we practise these behaviours, believing that they will not only make us feel better about ourselves, but also think better, of ourselves, and help to make the person we would like to be become reality.

Because we are fast learners, our habits can develop and become fixed very quickly. Take smoking, for example. Why did you first start smoking? From my experience of working with people who want to stop smoking, I have found that we often start because we think it looks cool. Many of us watch people smoking and we think it is an attractive and useful way to behave. However, the majority of us don't enjoy our first cigarettes – we often find them really uncomfortable and even painful. Yet we go through this pain because it is something that we want to do. The association that smoking is cool is learned and becomes more hardwired in our brains with each cigarette that is smoked.

You have not developed your smoking habit just for the sake of it. Your brain suggests to you what it thinks is best – what in the past might have alleviated some discomfort or seemed attractive at the time. You may have learnt to associate smoking with certain events or stimuli; for example, when you are feeling bored, tired or stressed, when you are out with friends, or when you are having a coffee. Whenever you experience any of your smoking 'triggers', it becomes an automatic response to smoke. For many of us, this has nothing to do with right and wrong, or good and bad, it is just something that we do.

For example, when some people are in a room full of strangers and they feel uncomfortable, their brain may suggest smoking because that is what has habitually made them feel more at ease. Because smoking is a behaviour that has worked before to alleviate discomfort in this situation, the brain has learned to see it as a solution and suggests it whenever any feelings of discomfort arise. The behaviour becomes habit.

Smoking is probably something you are good at – or may be even highly skilled at. It is often said that if you are skilled at something you can do it without even thinking about it, and this is a trap that many smokers fall into.

Eventually you reach the stage where you are merely going through the motions of this behaviour out of no more than habit. Are you like many other smokers who don't really enjoy smoking any more and want to stop, but don't feel that you CAN give up the habit?

Now Change is Possible

What do you think is the biggest hurdle for you to overcome when quitting smoking? For most people it is the simple fact that they don't like change.

Many find change uncomfortable even if there is a strong desire to do so. We are all very much creatures of comfort. You may have been stimulated to smoke for so many different reasons, all of which become a habit over time. Our brains go to great lengths to try and protect us from making changes, as they think that what we have been doing is what we are supposed to do.

The following exercise is called 'Thumbs' and it demonstrates how we instinctively regard change as uncomfortable.

1. Interlock your fingers, with one thumb sitting on top of the other thumb. Notice how that feels – it should feel pretty normal and comfortable.
2. Now unlock your hands and put them back together so that the other thumb is on top. How does that feel? The chances are that it feels distinctly uncomfortable, as though the wrong thumb is on top.
3. Now go back to the other, comfortable way – aaah, that probably feels better, as if this is how it is meant to be.

4. Interlock your fingers once again, with one thumb sitting on top of the other. Now switch the position of your thumbs back and forth at least 21 times, and as strange as this may seem, say either in your head or out loud, 'I love to change!'.

5. After 21 times, stop now and notice how it feels when you swap the position of your thumbs around – it will start to feel more comfortable.

This is a physical illustration of how the brain naturally directs us towards what it thinks is most comfortable. This might sound strange when applied to smoking, because you might not think that there is anything comfortable about continuing with your habit. It is possible, however, that stopping smoking is more uncomfortable than carrying on smoking. This is why the easiest course of action is to keep doing what you have done before. Your smoking habit is quite simply something you have practised, and whenever we try something that we don't normally do our brains complain – It's not me, it's not the way I do things.

In order to change a habit, you need to re-programme your brain. Do you want to rely on cigarettes for the rest of your life? Instead of smoking because it might make you feel better (temporarily), would you like to learn how to take control and be more responsible for your life, and learn how to focus your attention on more liberating ways of behaving?

In this book I will show you how to unlearn your habit of smoking and replace it with more productive and enjoyable ways of living your life. You will learn how to make simple but effective changes, and ultimately you will gain more control and become freer and happier.

About This Book

I am going to be completely straight and up front with you right from the start. How many people say they want to stop smoking, but when it actually comes to doing anything about it, they just make a half-hearted attempt and carry on smoking?

According to the US Department of Health and Human Services, 2/3 of people who are trying to give up start smoking again after 24 hours.

Only 2% of people who want to give up actually do so.

We first make our habits and then our habits make us.

JOHN DRYDEN

I have always been fascinated by the people who make up this 2%, many of them give up without any pain or trauma, and I have actively searched them out to find out the secrets of their success. I have found out what they did and how they did it. In this book I will reveal what I have discovered as I share the secrets of how to become an ex-smoker.

So are you one of the 70% of smokers in the UK who want to give up but just don't know where to start? Perhaps you have tried before and failed.

So why do so many people fail to become non-smokers? Perhaps they think it is too difficult, perhaps they rely on cigarettes too much, or perhaps they think that it is one of their few pleasures in life.

Whatever stopped you in the past from quitting doesn't really matter now – the past is past, so don't give yourself a hard time about it because all that matters right now is that you want to change.

However, it is important to think about how much you want to change and what you are prepared to do about it. Are you prepared to read this book and follow the simple instructions? How much effort are you going to put into the assignments that follow – 10%, 20% or 100%? It sounds obvious but the more effort you put in, the more you are going to get out of it.

Becoming a Special Agent

You may have smoked for so long and are so good at it you can do it without even thinking about it. If you were an actor you would probably deserve an award for playing the part of a smoker so well. But remember, smoking is something that you are *choosing* to do, it is just a part that you are playing, and you haven't been doing it all your life.

Just like Shakespeare said, the world is but a stage and we are all but actors upon that stage. Some people have literally played the part of the smoker to death, and their conviction and determination to smoke has been the death of them. I know this sounds tough, but it's true. Now it is time for you to lay this part to rest, before it lays you to rest, and take on board a more powerful role.

First, I'm going to challenge you to a mission. Your mission, if you choose to accept it, is to become a non-smoker. To help you do this you'll be taking on the role of a Special Agent. Special Agents are renowned for their cunning, their determination, their resourcefulness and their resilience. These are all qualities I am sure you possess and I will be referring to you as a Special Agent throughout the book. So right now, Special Agent, this is your mission – and don't worry, this book won't self-destruct in five seconds!

Why am I asking you to do this? Because I have found that this approach is effective and it works. The chances are that you have not adopted this method in previous attempts to quit smoking. Most people when they are trying to give up use the same old methods, which often involve struggle and hardship, but if you always do what you have always done, you will always get what you have always got.

The secret to change is doing things differently. I want you to see this as a mission that challenges and excites you as you take control of your life. In this book you will find 14 assignments, and within each assignment are one or two 'challenges' (habit-busting techniques and exercises) for you to work through over the next 21 days.

I have also inserted between some of the main challenges some quick and easy mini challenges to add a bit more fun to the process.

If you do your assignments and challenges with conviction, determination and desire they will have a positive effect on your life. Just like developing a habit, it is only by repeating, practising and applying the techniques, that you are going to get results.

Practise does not make perfect.
Practise makes permanent.

Perfect practise makes perfect. If you really want to change, you have to practise perfectly – that is, with attention and intention.

Your first challenge is to embrace the Special Agent's 'Three-word Success Course'.

The Three-Word Success Course

Everything you need to know about stopping smoking can be reduced to three simple words:

Can
Will
Now

Can
Can you do it? Do you possess the ability to stop smoking? The answer is yes! You are made up of over 10 billion cells. Science only understands about 5% of how the human mind and body works. You are infinitely more capable than you could ever have possibly imagined. You have powers buried deep inside you that you haven't discovered yet. You probably do not even realize just how amazing you really are.

Will

Will you use your own personal power, and are you willing and responsible enough to stop smoking? Just because you can does not necessarily mean you will. But through your own efforts and desire you *can* and you *will* stop smoking.

Now

When will you begin? Many people die with their best song unsung. Don't wait Special Agent; use the remarkable ability that you possess to kick the habit for good and start now.

Reality Check

What are you actually addicted to? In your mission to quit smoking there are two habits you need to break:

⊘   The physiological habit of nicotine addiction
⊘   The psychological habit of smoking

The first part of your mission is to overcome your addiction to nicotine. When you puff on a cigarette the nicotine goes to your brain and the craving that you have ends. But that only lasts for about 15 minutes. The satisfaction comes from overcoming the craving rather than from the nicotine itself.

Nicotine is not nearly as addictive as you think. Do you go for longer than 15 minutes without having a cigarette? For example, when you are on a bus or a plane, when you are at the cinema, or when you are with people who don't smoke.

Overcoming nicotine addiction is relatively straightforward and however you choose to wean yourself off it is your choice. Some people find that they can ease their withdrawal symptoms with patches and gums – if you think this will help you, then that's up to you.

However, the real challenge to becoming a non-smoker is overcoming the habit of smoking itself. This book will show you the way to achieve this goal.

Hard Facts

Throughout the book you will find some hard-hitting facts and figures about smoking. You may have heard some of them before, but at the same time dismissed them. Well, not now Special Agent. I have included these facts to remind you of the dangers of smoking, and I challenge you to read them slowly and accept that if you continue to smoke you probably will be making up these statistics one day.

But let's start on a lighter note – read through the following and become aware of what happens as soon as you stop.

What to Expect When You Stop Smoking

The good news about stopping smoking is that as soon as you finish your last cigarette your health can start to recover:

The following are **FACTS** that will help you to achieve your mission.

After 20 minutes: nicotine leaves your system; your pulse rate and blood pressure return to normal.

Within 8 hours: oxygen levels return to normal.

After 24 hours: carbon monoxide is eliminated from the body; lungs start to clear out mucus and other debris.

After 48 hours: nicotine is no longer detected in the body; sense of taste and smell returns to normal; nerve endings start re-growing.

After 72 hours: breathing becomes easier as the bronchial tubes relax; energy levels increase.

Within 2–12 weeks: circulation improves throughout the body making walking easier.

Within 3–9 months: breathing problems such as coughing and sinus congestion improve, shortness of breath and wheezing improve; overall lung function improved by 5–10%.

After a year: excess risk of coronary heart disease is half that of a smoker.

After 5 years: if you used to smoke 20 a day, risk of death from lung cancer has halved; stroke risk is reduced to that of a non-smoker.

Within 5–15 years: risk of cancer of the mouth and oesophagus is half that of a smoker.

Are you Ready for Your Mission?

Are you ready for action? What do you have in common with people who have successfully stopped smoking? The vast majority of successful quitters were highly dissatisfied with their smoking habit. Are you, like them, sick of being dependent upon something that is having such a negative effect on your life?

Successful quitters are people who are flexible and determined, and make an effort to overcome obstacles. They are willing to overcome discomfort and meet adversity and deal with it head on. You can do the same. I dare you to take control of your life, to turn it around and do more things to prolong it.

Special Agent, you might think that this is Mission Impossible, but in fact it is very much **MISSION POSSIBLE!** Some of the assignments and challenges in this book are very simple and straightforward. This might surprise you, especially if you have been smoking for a long time and believe that because your habit is complicated, the process of giving up will be difficult and complicated too.

You may have put a lot of time, money and energy into being a smoker. This is a big investment – if you had a pound for every time you had a cigarette, the chances are that you would be pretty rich. We live in a world where we pride ourselves on our investments, our money, cars and houses, and many of us would not want to let go of them. In order to quit smoking you will have to let go.

As you progress through your mission I want you to become increasingly conscious of what you are really giving up and, more importantly, what you are gaining.

When you choose to accept the assignments in this book, remember that you don't have to do them all straight away – you have got time to ensure that you are successful in your mission. You may find some of the assignments more useful then others, but accept the challenge to do all of them a few times before you exclude any.

Whenever you do any of the challenges in this book, you need to:

⊘ Ensure you are as free as possible from distractions.
⊘ Always have a notebook and pen handy.
⊘ Have cigarettes available to you, as I will be asking you to smoke during some of the assignments. If you have stopped smoking, you don't have to do this, but I still would like you to have a cigarette in your hand.

The Future is NOW

When preparing for action, it's important to decide how you are going to stop smoking. Often the most successful way is to make the choice to stop and just stop. Some smokers, however, find this method too abrupt and prefer to cut down gradually. If you plan to go this route, decide how many cigarettes you will smoke each day, making the number smaller each day until you stop for good.

It's entirely up to you but the sooner you start to stop, the sooner you will start to gain the benefits and the habits of a non-smoker. How many smokers say?:

'I'll give up tomorrow'
'I'll start on Monday'
'I'll give up for Lent'

This may work for some people, but remember, this is the future, right now, today. Tomorrow doesn't exist.

In order to quit for good, you need to be prepared. This book is about preparing you, and also giving you specific tools that will help you along the way. As I mentioned earlier, allow yourself 21 days to work through the assignments and challenges in this book to be successful in your mission.

Finally, remember to drink plenty of water in the weeks that follow as this helps to flush the nicotine and other toxic chemicals out of your body.

Good luck Special Agent, and remember I'm with you all the way ...

Pete Cohen

Always be a first-rate version of yourself, instead of a second-rate version of someone else.

JUDY GARLAND

What's in a Cigarette?

Tobacco smoke contains over 4,000 chemical compounds, which are present either as gases or as tiny particles. These include:

Nicotine	This is what is addictive. It stimulates the central nervous system, increasing the heart-beat rate and blood pressure. In large quantities nicotine is extremely poisonous.
Tar	Brown and treacly in appearance, tar consists of tiny particles and is formed when tobacco smoke condenses. Tar is deposited in the lungs and respiratory system and gradually absorbed. It is a mixture of many different chemicals, including: formaldehyde (used to preserve dead specimens), arsenic (used in rat poisons), cyanide (deadly poison) and polonium (cancer-causing radioactive element).

| Carbon monoxide | This binds to haemoglobin in the bloodstream more easily than oxygen does, thus making the blood carry less oxygen round the body. |

Tobacco is the only legally available consumer product that kills people when it is used entirely as intended.

Get into a Habit-Busting State

Special Agent, there is a very important first step to take in your mission to stop smoking. This is all to do with your state of mind, so whenever you do any of the assignments and challenges that follow, I want to show you how to get into the best state to be successful. Believe it or not, feeling relaxed and comfortable is one of the most effective states to be in, and one of the easiest ways to get into this state is to breathe deeply.

The Importance of Breath

Oxygen is the foundation of life; without it we die. Many of us breathe through our mouths, which does not properly filter the carbon dioxide. Many emotions such as stress, anxiety, worry and fear are made worse by incorrect breathing.

You may well think you have had a lifetime's worth of practice in breathing, but as anyone who has either theatrical or medical training will tell you, the more easily you allow air in and out of your body, the easier it will be for your brain and body to function.

Slow, deep breathing is one of the most natural and immediate ways to get into a relaxed state. When people are anxious or stressed, their breathing tends to be short and shallow and into the chest, rather than deep and incorporating the whole diaphragm. It may come as a surprise to you, but making a simple, subtle change to the way you breathe can have a profound impact on your state.

Challenge – Breathe Deeply

- Stop for a minute, now.
- Sit comfortably.
- Take three deep breaths.
- Allow the second and third breath to be deeper than those before.
- Just notice what happens.

Now, let's go one step further.

- Go and get a pen, right now, and make a mark two inches below your belly button and another four inches above.
- Now take another three or four slow, deep breaths, but this time filling up this area you have marked with air. Breathe in as much air as you can comfortably manage, and slowly breathe out.
- Breathing in this way helps you to relax as you are filling the lower part of your lungs with air and allowing more oxygen into your body.

Getting into State

When someone does a sport they need to warm up their body first to get it ready and focused for the challenge to come. Your brain is like a muscle – it needs to be warmed up before it starts to work. In most of the challenges that follow I will be asking you to do the following exercise first to get your brain warmed up and ready. This quick and simple exercise will help you to feel relaxed, yet in control, and will get you into the right state of mind for change. An icon representing this warm-up exercise (*) will appear before most other challenges, to remind you to do this one first.

Challenge – Getting into the Right State for Change *

1. Sit comfortably, focusing your attention back on your breathing so you are breathing between the two marks I asked you to make earlier.
2. Focus on the difference between an in breath and an out breath, as you allow your breathing rate to become slower and deeper.
3. Imagine you are breathing in feelings of relaxation and breathing out any tension or discomfort. As you breathe in now, imagine your breath travelling from your nose down to your toes, and as you breathe out imagine your discomfort disappearing through the soles of your feet.
4. The feeling you have now is the ideal state for change. You are likely to feel more positive and open to the possibility of change. You may feel calm, expectant, interested, alert, ready to go, excited.
5. Choose a specific word to describe how you feel at this moment – and practise letting this word drift effortlessly from your lips as you breathe out.

The more you do this exercise the more you will feel the way you want to feel. And the better you feel, the more control you will have. You probably breathe about 25,000 or more times a day, so I challenge you to breathe that little bit more deeply. Make a habit of breathing in this way as often as you can – how about 100 times today for starters?

This exercise is especially useful as your mission is to take on the persona of a non-smoker. Often people who smoke say they do it because it helps them to relax. In fact, the rush of nicotine does anything but relax them, as its effects are to put the body into a rapid state of stress. It is more likely that the act of taking a deep breath is what is helping them to relax.

Once you start breathing correctly you can start to realize that you don't need the toxins of the cigarette to achieve the same calming effect.

Mini Challenge – Time Out

When you are feeling particularly tired or stressed, perhaps during the course of a working day, stop whatever it is you are doing – this need take no longer than a minute. Either seated or standing, close your eyes. Straighten your back, keep your head erect, and relax your shoulders. Think of the thing you want most in the world. Picture yourself doing or having it – as though it has happened. Make the picture and feeling as real as you possibly can. Take a few deep breaths, open your eyes, and return to whatever you are doing in a more relaxed, happier and effective state of mind.

Make a Firm Commitment

What precedes all behaviours, actions and performances? What turns a dream into a reality? The answer is *choices*. Your choices determine what you think, how you feel, what you do and who you become.

It is often your choices, and not your conditions, that hold you back. If you make the decision to stop smoking and choose to make some different choices to the ones you are making now, you will succeed.

How come some people can break their habits while others can't? It is because they make different choices. They commit to achieving, and do whatever it takes to succeed.

That is why I want you to not only make a real choice to stop smoking, but also to make a contract with yourself. This will help to get you focused and committed to breaking your habit. It is your actions, remember, that will generate success.

Make a firm commitment to stop smoking, because commitment will unlock the energy to achieve it.

Contract

I, Special Agent_____

Will complete all the assignments in this book with determination, and add to my daily life those that work best for me.

Will honour my decision to stop smoking and become a happier and healthier person.

Can and will succeed.

Signed: _____

Dated: _____

The mind is the limit. As long as the mind can envision the fact that you can do something, you can do it, as long as you believe 100 per cent.

ARNOLD SCHWARZENEGGER

Watch What You Say

Many of the people I help to give up habits talk about having two sides to themselves: one that wants them to give up, and another which is able to persuade them to carry on. One woman came to see me because she thought she ought to give up smoking. She described the part of her that wished to give up as being her angelic and pure side who knew it would be better for her health, while the darker, more rebellious side wanted to keep her hooked on cigarettes, reasoning that she still enjoyed smoking and should not be dictated to by others. I find this scenario fairly typical among those who wish to stop smoking. They feel they should or ought to, and do not necessarily – to begin with, at least – actually want to. I asked this woman to tell me how she felt when she said: 'I should give up.' 'Completely demotivated', was her reply.

What words do you use to describe your mission to stop smoking?

Many people do not realize that the words they use about their intention can radically affect how they feel about quitting a habit. How many of us do the things we should do, and how many the things we want to?

Think about your own habit and say to yourself, for example: 'I should stop smoking.' Notice how it feels when you say this.

Now repeat this sentence, using each of the words in the list below.

I should
I ought to
I must
I have to
I'll try
I hope to
I could
I may
I might
I aim to

When you use words such as 'have to', 'need to' and 'must' they make you feel as though you are putting some unnecessary pressure on yourself. Words such as 'might,' 'may' and 'could' are very indecisive and are unlikely to inspire you to really go for it. When people use these words it doesn't give them a sense of conviction. They don't enthuse about their intention, because words really do affect how we think, feel and act. People often use might/may/could words because they have tried and failed to stop smoking before, and therefore feel it must be difficult. If this is how you have talked to yourself in the past, it doesn't surprise me that you have found stopping smoking difficult.

Now repeat this sentence, 'I _____ stop smoking' using each of the words in the list below. Notice which one makes you feel most motivated to change. I am not asking you to find which words make you believe you can change, just which feel best for you.

I challenge you, with the words you choose, to say this personalized sentence over and over to yourself, as if you really mean it, whether or not you believe it right now.

I will

I am going to

I can

I want to

I expect to

I have

Now, when you use these kinds of phrases ('I can be healthy,' I am a non-smoker,' 'I will control my own life,' 'I have the ability to quit smoking'), what do you picture? Think about what you want to achieve, not what you want to leave behind. See yourself as being already there.

The words you choose must, when you say them to yourself, make you feel as though you are actually going to live them. If they don't, it is unlikely they will be of much help, because breaking a habit is all about changing your feelings towards it, and yourself.

The words you choose about your intention must, when you say them to yourself, make you feel as though you are actually going to live them.

Mini Challenge – Talk Like a Special Agent
Many people talk about *giving up* smoking, but this can be quite a negative expression to use – people don't like to give up on anything. As a Special Agent *giving up* would not come into your vocabulary, as it can sound very weak. From now on I want you to say that you have quit or stopped smoking, or that you are a non-smoker. It's important to be clear that it is something that you have already

done, rather than something that you are doing but haven't finished yet. In the past there are probably some things that you did start but haven't truly finished. Smoking *isn't* going to be one of them.

What things soever ye desire, when ye pray, believe ye receive them, and ye shall have them.

MARK 11:24

Know Your Enemy

Special Agent, your next assignment is to learn what 'triggers' your desire to smoke. The assignment is divided into two parts – if you have already stopped smoking you don't need to do the first part, but if you are continuing to smoke whilst working through this book, then you will find it useful.

Part 1 – Keep a Record

Whenever a Special Agent is on an assignment they need to know what they are up against. In your case, in your mission to bust your smoking habit, you need to investigate what 'triggers' your desire to smoke. To do this, it is helpful to keep a written record of every cigarette that you smoke. Note down the time, what you were doing, and how you felt about that particular cigarette. This record is very useful, because until you become aware of what your habit is it is difficult to do something to change it.

Here's an example of how to keep the record. It's just an example; however you do it is fine, as long as you record each cigarette and what triggered you to smoke it.

Time	Activity – what triggered me to smoke?	Did I enjoy it?
7.00 am	Waking up – really wanted it to wake me up	Yes – first of the day
7.30 am	Walking to the train station – always have one now	Didn't notice
8.45 am	Walking from train station to office – the thought of not being able to have one for two hours	Not really – it was raining and only smoked half
10.30 am	Coffee break, standing outside office building – needed a break from the hassle of the office	Yes

And so on, throughout the day.

At the end of the day, make a note of all the different activities that you currently associate with smoking. Also include special occasions when you tend to smoke (for example, when you are on holiday), because even if they happen irregularly, if they occur and you aren't prepared for them, you might be tempted to slip back into old ways.

This will enable you to come up with a list of all the situations when you are triggered to smoke. For example:

1. First thing in the morning
2. Travelling to work
3. Coffee breaks
4. After meals
5. At the pub
6. When feeling stressed
7. When bored in the evenings
8. At parties if someone else is smoking

An awareness of what triggers you to smoke without even thinking about it will help you realize how automatic many of your responses have become, and how difficult it might have been in the past to change a behaviour that you didn't even realize that you were doing. When you start to become more aware of these patterns, then you can choose to do something different in each situation.

After you have kept the record for a few days, you will also see the times where you can avoid your smoking triggers, or if that's impossible, where you need to plan alternative ways to deal with the triggers.

Avoid your smoking 'triggers' or if that's impossible, plan alternative ways to deal with the triggers.

Part 2 – Choose a New Habit

Instead of going to the trouble of merely breaking your unwanted habit, choose a new one that serves you better. Get into the habit of saying, 'I'm not going to do *that* when I could do *this*' – and doing it! For example, if you find that you often have a cigarette with a cup of coffee first thing in the morning, try having something else to drink to break the association, for example, fresh fruit juice or hot water and lemon. If you stop one part of the habit, the other part won't seem to fit so well.

Think about what usually triggers or used to trigger you to smoke and come up with an alternative for each situation. So, for example:

Situation – what used to trigger me to smoke?	New habit to practise
When first wake up	Have a fruit juice and do some stretching
Travelling to work	Power walk the journey, listening to a personal stereo
Coffee breaks	Go to the staff canteen and read the paper
After meals	Clean my teeth
At the pub	Sit in the non-smoking area, play darts or snooker
When I am stressed	Learn deep breathing exercises
When I am bored in the evenings	Take the dog for a walk, telephone a non-smoking friend for support, plan my next holiday, join a gym, start an evening class
At parties if someone else is smoking	Make a point of talking to non-smoking guests, stand in rooms where I am with non-smokers

Look for alternative habits that will give you more than the habit you are giving up. If you replace smoking with something you don't enjoy, the chances are that you won't keep it up, and you will be more tempted to go back to your old ways.

Remember that stopping smoking is going to give you more time, not only in the time freed from actually smoking, but also in the extra years of life that being a non-smoker is going to give you. I hear so many people saying that they wished they had more time, so you are actually giving yourself a great gift – what are you going to do with it?

Use Your Imagination

I've already mentioned the importance of making a choice to stop smoking, because it is your choice that unlocks the action necessary to break a habit. The main tool that is going to help you is learning how to use your mind in more powerful and productive ways. And the first step in doing this is learning how to use your imagination.

The imagination is such an effective tool because what we can imagine we can achieve. Our brains cannot distinguish between a real and an imagined event, so they can be fooled into believing that something that we create or invent in our minds is real. Have you ever woken up after a dream and thought that the dream was real, and then it dawned on you that it wasn't?

The following challenge demonstrates how you can use your mind in a powerful way.

Challenge – Creating a Full Sensory Experience

Part 1

1. Sit comfortably, free from distractions, keeping your eyes open or closed, whichever suits you.
2. Remember the best holiday you have ever had.
3. Recall some of the things you saw or heard on this holiday, the things you smelled and tasted, and some of the things you felt.
4. Imagine being back on that holiday now.
5. Make it more real and more colourful even than you remember it.
6. Now take a couple of deep breaths. Feeling good, slowly open your eyes.
7. Take a short break, and then close your eyes again (if you wish).

Part 2

1. Now imagine being on a make-believe holiday.
2. Imagine you are on a beautiful beach with white sand and clear blue water.
3. You can hear the gentle sound of the waves and the seagulls calling out high in the sky.
4. You can smell the sea air and almost taste the salt.

5. You feel warm, peaceful and relaxed.
6. Take a deep breath and open your eyes.

Although you know the difference, your brain cannot distinguish between the real and the imagined holiday. The more you think about the one you made up, the more your brain starts to think that it is real.

The Power of the Imagination

Simply imagining an event or great experience has an effect on the body. In an experiment conducted for a science-based television programme, a group of people were told to regularly imagine doing exercise. Although the difference was tiny, small muscle definition was detected a few weeks later, and all the control group had used to change their body shape was their minds.

This might sound amazing, but if we think about it, the nervous system that connects the whole body starts in the brain, which sends messages to and collects messages from the rest of the body. It actually makes sense that what happens in one will have an effect in the other.

Because the nervous system cannot distinguish between a real and an imagined experience, if practised enough, the thoughts we have become a plan of what we are going to do. And the more clearly thought-out and distinctive our desire, the more passionately we will pursue it.

Everyone uses their imagination all the time, but not necessarily in particularly effective or productive ways.

If I were to ask you:

⊘ What did you have for dinner last night?
⊘ Where was your last holiday?
⊘ What colour is an orange?
⊘ What does your best friend look like?

You'd immediately make a picture of them.

Using your imagination in this way is also known as 'visualization'. I prefer to call it *effective thinking*. Visualization is not a technique – as I have shown, you already do it every day. It is how human beings process information about their world. The difference is how you *use* this in-built skill.

One of the keys to stopping smoking is to start imagining your life in the future, free from the habit, doing things differently, and being in control. You get what you focus on.

The soul never thinks

without a picture.

ARISTOTLE

See Yourself as a Non-smoker

Some people are naturally more visual than others, but we can all learn to visualize effectively. Visualization can be a very powerful technique when we put it to particular use, such as seeing yourself having broken the habit of smoking, and we will be using it quite a lot in the assignments that follow.

Let me ask you a question, can you see yourself or imagine yourself as a non-smoker – being more relaxed and in control?

The chances are that it is easy to imagine yourself smoking, because it is something that you have practised and are good at. But can you imagine yourself having broken the habit? Can you picture this clearly? Can you see yourself in all the instances during which you smoke, not smoking?

I was sitting in a sauna one day listening to a man telling his friend how impossible he found it to give up smoking. After about 10 minutes of listening to his complaining I stopped him and asked him if he could imagine himself in the future, in all the particular instances during which he smokes, not smoking. He said no. This was why he was finding it so difficult to stop.

If you want to bust your habit, you need to be able to see yourself how you want to be. In other words, you need to be able to see yourself as already having quit smoking. In order for you to be successful in your mission, you need to be able to wear the disguise of a non-smoker without being detected and play the part convincingly in a variety of situations (for example, when you are out with friends or during coffee breaks at work). The more you can use your imagination to help you in this, the more successful you are likely to be, because by imagining yourself as vividly as possible as this ex-habit person, you are allowing your body to prepare for the end result.

The time has come for you to realize that you have more potential than you ever thought.

Challenge – Stepping into the Future

1. Get into the habit-busting state * (see page 26).
2. Stand up and give yourself some space. Now close your eyes.
3. Imagine that your front door is right in front of you, life-size.
4. On the other side of the door is an image of you, in the future, having quit smoking. In a moment I want you to imagine that the door opens and you will be looking at the back of yourself.

5. Imagine that the door opens, right now, and you can see this life-size image of yourself. Notice the difference in how you look. See this image of the future you in as much detail as you like. Imagine that the image is turning around so you can see it from the side and then the front. Look how much more vibrant and full of life this future you is.

6. See this future you in as much detail as you like, as you move the image of yourself around so you are looking at your back again.

7. Now I want you to imagine stepping into this image of the future you, so you are seeing through the eyes of a non-smoker and you are feeling how it feels to be in control.

8. Do this again, but this time, physically take a step forwards as if you were trying on a new skin or a new suit.

9. Feel the changes in every cell of your body. Notice how much more freely you breath, and all the other benefits you've gained from quitting the habit.

10. Once you have finished, take a few deep breaths and have a break.

Doing this exercise on its own doesn't make much difference, but the brain is like a muscle and the more you exercise it, the more it starts to see what it is you would like to happen. Just like an actor preparing for a role, you are visualizing yourself playing the part of a non-smoker and practising the role again and again until you are so good at it you forget you are acting at all. So *practise this exercise every day*, and take this image of the future you wherever you go.

Doing this should also make you feel good, and because making you feel good is one of the brain's primary functions, the thought or imagining becomes a way of behaving that the brain wishes to adopt.

When you commit yourself mentally to changing a habit, and start practising having made that change, the change will happen. You could just as easily decide not to, but those who really want to change will work at it repeatedly until they get the desired result.

If one desires a change, one must be that change before that change can take place.

GITA BELLIN

You Are One of These Statistics, or You Could Be

FACT: Smoking increases the risk of having a heart attack by two to three times, compared to the risk to non-smokers.

FACT: Smoking causes 30% of all cancer deaths (including at least 80% of lung cancer deaths).

FACT: About half of all regular smokers will eventually be killed by their habit.

Increase Your Motivation

What is motivating you to stop smoking?

One of the things that I have discovered is that for the 2% of people who do successfully quit, their main motivation is that they have had enough of the discomfort their habit is causing them. Are you affected by any of the following?

- ⊘ The physical effects of smoking, for example, not being able to breathe properly or a cough that never seems to go away.
- ⊘ The shock of a diagnosis of cancer or heart disease or another life-threatening illness.
- ⊘ The unpleasant physical signs of smoking, for example, the stench of your breath, clothes and hair; the yellowing of your teeth; your skin aging quicker than normal.

⊘ The financial cost, not only of the cigarettes, but also insurance premiums.

⊘ The social cost, for example, being a social leper; not being able to smoke at work; having to stand outside in the rain when visiting non-smoking relatives.

Are you motivated by one of the above, or all of them, or are there other reasons why you want to quit?

Let me ask you another question. On a scale of 1 to 100, how high is your desire to become a non-smoker? You may be like most people who have a strong desire to quit but find that your motivation to actually follow through isn't as powerful.

You may think that desire is the same thing as motivation, but it's not. Motivation is what propels you to take action. You may desire to stop smoking, but when it comes to doing anything about it, you lack the motivation to achieve your goal.

Another way of looking at it is illustrated by this story of the man who prayed to win the lottery.

'Please goddess, let me win the lottery today,' he prayed.

'OK,' said the goddess.

When the man didn't win he prayed again, asking for success next week.

'Yes, alright,' said the goddess, but another week passed and still the man hadn't won.

When he asked the goddess again, she said, 'For goodness sake, meet me half way ... buy a ticket!'

You may think that this book is your winning ticket and shows your desire to change, but the real winning ticket is whether you are motivated and willing to take some simple but highly effective steps to quit smoking forever.

One reason why your motivation may not be as high as your desire is because of failed attempts to stop smoking in the past. Another reason may be that you still get pleasure and enjoyment from smoking. Both can chip away at your motivation.

Your challenge is to understand that one of the best things about the past is that it is over, and I want you to leave your failed attempts to stop in the past where they belong.

Moving Towards Your Goal

Would you like to feel 100% motivated to stop smoking? If the answer is yes, great, because I am about to share with you one of the most powerful exercises I use to help people to stop – I am going to get you to think about the consequences of continuing with your habit.

As I mentioned earlier, most people want to stop smoking out of disgust and discomfort with themselves and their habit. One way to motivate ourselves to stop is to turn up the pain – in other words, to think about what the future would be like should we still be smoking. It is often the serious thought of the discomfort of *not* taking action that make us want to take action.

Motivation is really no more than persuading ourselves to do whatever it is we want to do. We have all had some experience of being motivated; we simply have to learn how to put that feeling to work in the direction we want. To do this, we have to make what we want to do so compelling, and what we no longer want to do so repellent, that we are eager to get on and do the new thing and abandon the old NOW.

A well-known example of this would be the story of Ebenezer Scrooge in the 'Christmas Carol'. When Scrooge sees how his future will turn out if he doesn't change his ways, he not only becomes frightened, he also becomes extremely motivated to do whatever it takes to make certain that possible future doesn't become reality.

Have you ever stopped for a moment and really thought about the long-term consequences of failing in your mission to quit smoking?

Turn up the pain of not taking action so it gets you to the point that you think: I have got to do something about this.

Challenge – Generating Motivation to Stop Smoking

The following challenge, Special Agent, is designed to get you to change your feelings towards your habit, so that the thought of smoking starts to disgust you. If you find this challenge too intense you can stop at any time.

The exercise is divided into two parts. The first part is designed to get you to imagine what would happen if you did not stop smoking, thus propelling you away from a possible grim future. And the second part helps you to see what life will be like once you have stopped smoking. In this part of the exercise you will be imagining a brighter, healthier future, as you see yourself having kicked the habit for good.

To get maximum benefit from the first part of the exercise, you need to have a cigarette in your hand. I recommend that you light the cigarette. You don't have to smoke it if you don't want to, but having it burning in your hand will increase the effect.

It would also be highly beneficial to get someone to read this exercise to you slowly and carefully, or tape-record yourself reciting it.

Part 1

1. Sit comfortably.
2. Get into the habit-busting state * (see page 26).
3. Light the cigarette.
4. Think about your smoking habit and how much discomfort smoking is already causing you. You may find this easier with your eyes closed, but if you do be careful of the cigarette.
5. Think now about the consequences of what would happen if you continue to smoke.
6. Imagine you have continued to smoke for another six weeks. See yourself looking in a mirror. Is your health better or worse? Do you feel positive or disappointed that you have continued smoking? As you are looking in the mirror, are you standing tall or are you standing ashamed? What sort of things would you say to yourself? Would you be upbeat or despondent?
7. Now take the feeling of discomfort you get from having carried on indulging in this destructive habit for another six weeks, and imagine yourself still smoking in six months' time.
8. You have dragged with you into the future every cigarette you have smoked and all the misery of having continued to smoke. See yourself in front of the mirror again.

9. What is your health and well-being like? Do you have more energy or less energy? What about your posture? Look at yourself, your complexion, the colour of your skin, and the expression on your face. Do you feel upbeat or despondent?

10. How do you feel about yourself now? What do you say about yourself? What are other people saying about you?

11. Now imagine you have continued smoking for a year. All that pain and discomfort, and all the effects that puffing on all those cigarettes has had on you is magnified by another 365 days, as you look once more into the mirror. Do you like what you see? Is your health better or worse? Imagine you can look inside yourself and notice your lungs, your heart and every cell of your body, as you become aware of the damage that smoking has done to you. Has smoking made you lighter or darker inside? What about your complexion and the colour of your skin. Do you like what you see? Do you feel upbeat or down?

12. Have a really good look at yourself from head to toe, and really notice the effects smoking has had on you and your overall health and well-being.

13. Imagine that you have continued to smoke for another five years, again hauling with you every cigarette you have smoked, so you can feel the effects of every puff from

every cigarette you have smoked. Imagine the ash from all the cigarettes you have smoked around you. How is your health – better or worse?

14. Do you like what you have become? How do you feel about yourself? What does the face you see tell you about you?

15. Now take the consequences of having behaved in that way and think about what you will be like in another 10 years, if you carry on smoking.

16. Look at yourself in the mirror. Look at what you can see in that reflection and notice how you sound and feel, having continued to smoke for all this time. Do you like what you see? Do other people like what they see? What do they say about you? What do you say about yourself?

17. Do you want to be this person in 15 years' time? You could easily be this person if you choose to continue with this destructive, dangerous habit.

Stop now for a moment and take a deep breath, and be thankful that none of what you have imagined has happened.

Now let me ask you a question. Do you feel more motivated to stop smoking now you have done this exercise – yes or no?

Remember in the 'Christmas Carol' story, Scrooge felt motivated to change his ways because he saw how miserable his future was going to be if he didn't take action. Are you like Scrooge in that you used to be able to stand the day-to-day discomfort of smoking, but now when you think of the consequences of continuing to smoke, you feel compelled to quit for good?

If you don't, I recommend you go back and do this exercise over and over again, until you are.

You can change what has not yet occurred. That was only an imagined future. It could happen, but it does not have to. You get what you focus on.

Are you 100% motivated to stop smoking?

When you know you are ready to change your behaviour after doing this exercise, take a short break: have something to drink or go for a walk.

Having taken a sufficient rest, take four or five deep breaths before moving on to the second part of this challenge.

It's time to turn up the pleasure of how much better you will feel once you have kicked your habit for good.

Part 2

1. Sit comfortably.

2. Get into the habit-busting state *.

3. Think about your smoking habit and how much pleasure you would get from breaking it. As before, you may find this easier with your eyes closed.

4. Imagine now that you have stopped smoking for three days. See yourself looking in the mirror. Notice how much better you feel as you really have started to kick the habit, and the nicotine cravings have gone away.

5. Now imagine that you have stopped smoking for 21 days. What are the benefits? Look at yourself in the mirror. Is your health worse or better? Do you feel disappointed or proud of your achievement? What sort of things do you say to yourself? How upbeat are you?

6. Now imagine you have stopped smoking for six weeks. Look at yourself in the mirror once more. How do you feel now? What is your health like? Do you have less energy or more energy? And what about your complexion and your skin? Notice how much colour you have. Do you like what you see? What do you say to yourself?

7. Now take the feeling of satisfaction that you get from having stopped smoking for six weeks, and go six months into the future. Imagine that you can turn up that feeling of

satisfaction, and take with you all of the pleasure you have gained from having better health and well-being.

8. Look in the mirror. Notice how upbeat and positive you are.

9. Now imagine you have stopped smoking for 365 days. Imagine once again looking in the mirror. All of the pleasure and joy is magnified by each of these days. Look at the colour of your skin and your complexion. Imagine you can see inside yourself now. Are you darker or lighter? What sort of things are you saying to yourself?

10. Now imagine going even further into the future, five years from now. The habit is a distant memory. Do you have less energy or more energy? Be aware of how much more freely you can breathe.

11. You arrive in front of the mirror. Have a look at what you can see in the reflection, and how it feels to be free and in control.

12. How do you feel about yourself? How do people who you are important to feel about you?

13. Notice how much more confident you feel.

14. Now you are 10 years into the future, free from the habit, and you see yourself in the mirror.

15. Once again, be aware of what you can see and feel.

16. Listen to what you say about yourself, what others say about you, and notice how it feels to have been living for 10 years without this habit. You are positive and in control; you have more energy and feel so alive.

17. Now, slowly take a few deep breaths. With each breath, breathe in that confidence you now feel. Notice how good you feel: in control and relaxed.

Congratulations! What you have seen is all there waiting to happen. Now that you can see it, you can start to believe it.

Remember, you need to do these motivation exercises as many times as it takes to get you ready to change your behaviour. For many people these exercises are often enough to get them to make that change. But if you are still not motivated to stop smoking for good, go back and do them again and again until you know that you are.

You cannot teach people anything. You can only help them to discover it within themselves.

GALILEO

Focus on What You Want

Instead of thinking about what they would *like* to happen, most smokers, when trying to break their habit, focus on how hard it is to quit. Images come to mind of their many failed attempts in the past, and of the pain and trauma of withdrawing themselves from what they think is a highly addictive substance, and they hype this all up so much that it becomes an insurmountable obstacle that is not worth trying to overcome. Special Agent, I don't want you to have to jump over obstacles, I want you to work around them by focusing on what you want to have happen.

Are you ready for your next assignment? You say you want to free yourself from your smoking habit, and have read this far. Are you ready now to use your imagination to help you focus on what you would like to happen? Write down what you want to achieve.

I want _____

If in the space above you have written 'I want to stop smoking,' what are you thinking about? You are probably making a picture in your mind of smoking or you smoking.

To show you what I mean I want you *not* to think of a blue elephant. What immediately comes to mind – a blue elephant? This is because in order not to think of something your mind makes a picture of it first. So when you say you want to stop smoking, smoking will still stay part of the picture.

The effect of this is to leave you focused on what you don't want, which is why you have probably found stopping in the past so difficult. The picture that comes to mind as you write out your description is of you doing the habit you want to break. Now it's time for you to use a different approach, because a simple rule of life is you get what you focus on. So if you are focusing on smoking and how hard it is to give it up, then the chances are that you will never give it up.

Your challenge is to do what people who have successfully given up smoking do. They have learnt to focus on the very thing they want, for example, 'to be in control', 'to be healthy', 'to be more relaxed', 'to be more confident', 'to be able to breathe easier'. They do this because it brings to mind images of how they want to be. This is more compelling to them than focusing on the habit itself.

Once more, write down in the slot what you want to achieve, but this time what you want to achieve, *specifically*. By writing it down and repeating it out loud you will be creating a representation of something that you want your brain to find more evidence to support. This is what really can set you free from your habit.

Sometimes we need to work harder than other times to create this image, but one thing is clear, when you give your brain an image of what you want, you are then opening up yourself to its possibility. If you can see it, you start to think of thoughts as tangible. Look at all the things around you in your home – your television, telephone, toaster – none of these have existed since the beginning of time, whenever that was. Someone had an idea, made a picture in their mind of what they wanted to be able to do, and created something that would be able to fulfil that wish.

Getting What You Want

Your brain can only follow the instructions you give it. To override your smoking habit, you need to give the brain a new set of well thought-out and quite specific instructions, over and over again. The instructions, or new goal(s), need to be so attractive that your brain wants to leave behind your habit and move towards the new you.

In order to get what you want, you need to KNOW what you want. You must be as clear as you can be about what it is you want to achieve. What pictures come to mind? Do you have a clear idea of your own direction?

In order to get what you want, you need to KNOW what you want.

Challenge – Setting Your Direction

Get your notebook and have your list of what you want to achieve in front of you. Get into the habit-busting state*.

Once you are satisfied with the idea of what you want to achieve, say it out loud to yourself and picture yourself as already having achieved it. Then, sitting somewhere comfortably, with ample time at your disposal and perhaps playing your favourite music, answer the following questions:

1. What do I want, specifically?
2. When, where and with whom do I want it?
3. What will be different as a result of me stopping smoking?

4. How will I know when I have quit for good?
5. What will stopping smoking do for me?
6. How do I feel about stopping smoking?
7. Once I have quit, what will be different about what I will see, hear and feel?
8. What will happen if I stop smoking?
9. What would be the consequences of me continuing to smoke?
10. How do I know that stopping is worth it?
11. What effect will stopping smoking have on my life, my family, my job and my friends?

The answers will give you a clearer vision of what you want and the direction you are going to go in. You may want to go through these questions a few times, as they will help to build up your motivation to spur you into action.

A mission could be defined as an image of a desired state that you want to get to. Once fully seen, it will inspire you to act, fuel your motivation and determine your behaviour.

CHARLES GARFIELD

Create Your Own Inner Coach

What do you think is the most common habit of those who live in the Western world?

It's not smoking, or eating too much or getting stressed. These of course are very common habits, but the biggest habit by far is people giving themselves a hard time and mentally beating themselves up.

A friend of mine once coached a very famous French football player. One day he asked him, 'Do you ever give yourself a hard time?' The player, who did not speak great English, looked a little confused, so my friend asked whether he ever talked to himself inside his head when he made a mistake. The confused look on the player's face now became dazed, but after a few minutes he shouted out: 'Ahhh, you mean zee duck in my head.'

It was now my friend's turn to be confused, but after a short time he realized what the Frenchman was really saying. My friend replied, 'Yes, that's right, the duck.'

Now not everyone has a duck in their head but everyone talks to themselves.

My friend then said to this player 'Have you ever thought about telling the duck to shut up?' This question made the player laugh, but at the same time he became aware that he could soften this voice so that it was not critical and judgmental.

The quality of our lives comes down to how well we communicate with ourselves. If we are gentle and kind to ourselves we feel good about ourselves and the opposite is true if we are hard on ourselves.

Do you remember when you were a child? Did you have an imaginary friend or pet, or did you ever imagine that you were a doctor or a nurse or a fireman? I want you to use that same imagination to create your own Inner Coach.

I always encourage people who want to quit smoking to do this – to create a made-up coach inside their heads whose job is to keep them focused on breaking their habit. Their coach's responsibility is to take care of them and help them to quit smoking for good.

So your next assignment Special Agent is to create and design your own Inner Coach.

Designing Your Own Inner Coach

Get your notebook so you can write down your ideas.

What sort of voice would you like your Inner Coach to have? It could be like a motivational speaker's voice that inspires and keeps you positive. It could be soft and gentle, keeping you calm and relaxed. Or perhaps it could be seductive and sexy like Barry White.

Play around with your Inner Coach and give it time to operate in the way that works best for you. Be patient, as this idea of taking care of yourself in this way may be a little strange.

Your Inner Coach's Responsibilities

1. To be positive.
2. To be encouraging at all times and to stamp out any worries or concerns.
3. To be gentle and kind to you – not criticizing you, judging you or giving you a hard time.
4. To keep you focused on your outcome – for you to be in control and relaxed, having busted your smoking habit for good.

5. To keep you on track with your mission and to ma[ke]
   you follow through with the assignments and challen[ges]
   this book.

6. To remind you – in a way that is instantaneous and
   powerful – of your desire to stop smoking if you are
   tempted to smoke. For example, you could do the
   challenge in Assignment 9.

7. To always put things back into perspective with reassuring
   words.

8. To get you to relax and keep a positive perspective by
   reminding you to breathe deeply and slowly.

9. To use the mantra of 'Shut the Duck Up' to cancel out any
   doubting voices you might hear in your head.

10. To remind you to celebrate every day that you are getting
    stronger.

11. To help you by suggesting alternative things that you can
    do instead of smoking that make you feel good (see
    Assignment 4 for suggestions).

12. To deal with setbacks and possible lapses in a
    constructive and forward-thinking manner (see
    Assignment 12).

With the help of your Inner Coach, pay more attention to your internal dialogue and become more aware of what you say to yourself and how you treat yourself. If you find you are talking to yourself in a negative or derogatory manner, tell yourself to 'Shut the Duck Up', then give yourself some encouragement and be kind, as you would be to a child or a best friend.

Mini Challenge – Ask Yourself Empowering Questions

When trying to break a smoking habit, be aware of the type of questions you ask yourself. Most people ask themselves the wrong questions, such as:

'*Why* can't I give up smoking?'
'*Why* do I always fail?'
'*Why* is it so hard?'

The brain will only ever try to offer a helpful answer – there are always endless reasons why we can't do something! But to get from it a far more effective and useful answer, we need to learn to explore our own potential to help ourselves by asking '*What*' and '*How*' questions, such as:

'*What* could I be doing to gain control and stop smoking?'
'*How* I can feel good?'
'*What* can I do if someone offers me a cigarette?'

Remember, what you think about is what you tend to get. You set the direction you want to take. So get into the habit of asking yourself empowering questions.

Have a Fag!

One day I was discussing the effects of smoking with a friend of mine, who is a surgeon, and I was reeling off some of the dangers that I knew. He stopped me in my tracks and said that when you look inside the body of a smoker, you realize that smoking equals one thing and one thing only, and that is death. He explained that smoking kills the body, not only the lungs but also every single cell, as it starves the body of the oxygen and nutrients it needs.

Special Agent, the following challenge is a powerful way of changing the way you think about smoking forever. Be prepared, it may have a profound effect on you and only do it if you are serious about busting your habit.

Challenge – Say *Blurhhhhhh!*

I want you to sit in a comfortable place with a cigarette in your hand for the following exercise. If you have already stopped smoking, then still hold the cigarette and light it up for maximum impact. If you are still smoking, then I encourage you to smoke for this challenge.

I want you to face your smoking habit head on – look at it and size it up. Ask yourself exactly what it is doing for you; then ask yourself what it is not doing for you. You can work your way from the top of your head to the tips of your toes – it's a medical fact that smoking affects every organ in the human body.

Take the first lug of the cigarette. Breathe the smoke in deeply and as you do read the following.

FACT: Over 330 people will die today in the UK as a direct result of smoking.

FACT: Over 26,000 people die from coronary heart disease in the UK every year as a direct result of smoking.

FACT: a smoker is 50% more likely to contract cancer than someone who doesn't smoke.

Take another puff now.

Now you could say that none of this will ever happen to you. But I want you to consider some of the other effects that smoking has on you. Right now, as you are smoking, your heart is working much harder. It could be beating up to 10,000 extra beats today just because you are smoking. Why? Because you are struggling right now to combat the effects of the nicotine restricting your arteries. Your blood pressure is increasing as your body is making a great effort to deliver oxygen to your vital organs.

Take another puff now, as you consider whether this cigarette is really helping you to relax.

That smoke that is going down into your lungs is also carrying with it in excess of 4,000 chemical compounds. And just in case you did not know, many of these are poisonous. According to recent information released by the government, cigarettes contain: a paint stripper, a toilet cleaner, a lighter fuel, the chemical in mothballs, a poison used in gas chambers, a rocket fuel, and many other deadly poisons.

Take another puff.

But please also remember the chemical fertilizers and insecticides that are sprayed on the tobacco crops, that are now being absorbed into your body tissues.

Take another puff, if you still want to continue smoking the cigarette.

That cigarette you are smoking is adding to the toxic coating of thick, sticky tar that is already inside your lungs. This is clogging your lungs up and stopping you from taking in oxygen. Your whole body is being suffocated. The cigarette that you are smoking right now is stopping many of your tissues in your body receiving enough oxygen. Your arteries are becoming constricted and blocked

Take another puff.

What about the taste and the smell, that at times you have chosen to ignore? Now bring your full attention to it. Put the cigarette in your other hand, and smell and look at your fingers, and see where the cigarette has stained them. Rub your tongue over your teeth and be aware of how smoking has stained your teeth and damaged your gums.

Take another puff.

Right now become aware of the stinking, stale tobacco-laden breath that smoking gives you.

Take another puff.

The cigarette that you are smoking right now is ageing your skin. Feel the skin on your face, as you become aware that the skin of a smoker ages faster than that of a non-smoker.

Take another puff.

This cigarette is reducing your life expectancy by more than six minutes. Twenty cigarettes a day reduces your life by two hours.

You can choose to carry on smoking this cigarette right now or you can put it out in disgust.

You are now more aware of the serious damage smoking is doing to you. When doing this exercise, many people get to the point where they become so disgusted by smoking that they make a 'blurhhhhh' sound.

The next step is for you to also make that sound. Go for it!

Blurhhhhhhhh.

Now do it again but this time louder and with more feeling.

Every time you are 'triggered' to smoke, I want you to remind yourself in a way that is instantaneous and powerful of the nauseating smell, the disgusting taste and the serious damage to your health.

To help you with this, your next assignment Special Agent is to immediately make that

Blurhhhhhhhhhhhhhhhhhhhhhhhhh

sound every time you think of a cigarette or are offered one. As silly as this may seem, if you practise it regularly you will change your associations to smoking forever and you will find it much easier to become a non-smoker.

Remember – cigarettes are not a familiar friend but more like a greedy parasite demanding constant attention. You need to kill the parasite, because without you, the host, it cannot survive. If you choose to reject it, it will have no power.

Do You Want to Kill Someone You Love?

FACT: More than 17,000 babies and children under the age of five are admitted to hospital every year because of the effects of passive smoking – breathing other people's tobacco smoke.

FACT: It is estimated that several hundred cases of lung cancer and several thousand cases of heart disease in non-smokers in the UK are caused by passive smoking – breathing other people's tobacco smoke.

FACT: Passive smoking already kills more non-smokers than motor vehicle accidents, all crimes, AIDS, illegal drugs, etc. In other words, people are statistically more likely to die as a result of drifting tobacco smoke than by a car, a gun or the AIDS virus.

Believe That You CAN Quit

Special Agent, your next assignment is a very important one because until you can *truly* believe that you can stop smoking, you are going to find it very difficult to succeed in your mission.

One of the brain's many functions is to confirm what we believe. What many people often do automatically is look out for anything that substantiates their ideas about themselves and the world. So if you believe something is possible, you will create the behaviour that supports this belief. Our brains are always actively engaged in perpetuating what is happening now. It happens automatically. You choose what is happening in your head, and your brain generates more of it.

If you expect stopping smoking to be difficult, it probably will be. But when you believe you are capable of change and are actually changing, your attention is focused on this message, which reinforces the new, positive belief. Until you can believe you can break the habit, you are going to find it very difficult to succeed, because belief and behaviour are intrinsically linked.

If you truly believe you can stop smoking, you act in ways that support the belief.

Focusing on a Positive Belief

A woman came to see me once because she wanted to give up smoking. She had tried before, she told me, and always failed because it was too difficult and she had no willpower. She did not believe, based on past evidence, that she could. Before she went on, I asked her if she could imagine herself in the future not smoking. She said she could not. I told her she would find it difficult to break the habit if she could not even imagine herself being able to break it.

To help her to build a belief, I asked her to remember and tell me about all the times in her life when she had persisted at something. She said she managed to learn to drive and pass her test at 25. Had she ever considered giving up, even though she was older than many who learn and find it difficult? I asked. No, she replied. She also told me about how she managed to study and complete a degree while married with two children, and how she had been there to help a friend through a period of serious illness.

I then asked her to imagine making a movie of these experiences so she could watch herself as though it was a film on a large screen. 'I am doing this,' I told her, 'because I want you to realize how capable you really are and to start believing that you can give up smoking.' She imagined the movie, which as soon as it ended began again, over and over and over. With each screening the movie became more real and, when she had watched for a while, she felt good about herself. I then asked her what she would say about the person in the movie. After some thought, she said: 'They are hot, they can do anything.' Then I told her to make the statement her own, so 'They can do anything' became 'I can do anything.' Repeating this affirmation, she then imagined the movie again, only this time she stepped into it and made it even more dramatic, like an Indiana Jones or a James Bond film. I told her to watch herself as the star and, whenever the movie finished, to start it from the beginning again straightaway. On each replay the colour, sound and acting qualities were enhanced further and further, so the events were as real as when they had actually occurred.

This exercise put her into a really powerful state and gave her the foundation of the belief that she really could stop smoking. Once she had been able to remember and again believe she could do anything, she was able to stop.

When you go to see a movie, particularly an action film, the director is trying to give you an experience through all of your senses. Much the same thing is happening with the following challenge: you are making up an experience that just happens to be true. As well as proving to you just how capable you are, we will also develop from this exercise an affirmation – a positive statement about yourself you know to be true, which will help you to achieve your goal.

Challenge – Building a Powerful Belief

If you truly believe you can stop smoking, you act in ways that support the belief. This challenge is designed to help you build the belief that you can change.

You might find doing the second part of this challenge easier with your eyes closed and with someone else reading it out to you, or you could tape-record it yourself.

Doubt is a pain too lonely to know that faith is his twin brother.

KAHLIL GIBRAN, *THE PROPHET*

Part 1

1. Get your notebook and, giving yourself plenty of time with perhaps some music playing in the background, write down as many instances as you can of times in your life when you:

    – performed well at a task
    – were praised for a task
    – persisted in the face of obstacles or difficulties
    – gave 100% to some project
    – learned and mastered a new skill.

    It could be any moment, and the event could be or might seem to be trivial. One of my earliest memories of a moment of achievement is being able to tie my shoelaces, but it could be anything: the way you work, how you keep your house in order, what you do as a hobby, the way you dealt with a potentially self-damaging situation, the day you passed your driving test or bought a house or tiled the bathroom.

    Take time to recall and write down all the events you can remember. It does not matter if it takes a few days. Aim to have about 30 on your list.

2. When you have a nice long list, read them all through as though it were a list of achievements of someone you have never met.

3. Now choose the five of which you are most proud. These are the ones that, when you think about them, give you the best feeling.

4. Arrange them in your mind so one event can follow another (not necessarily in chronological order), almost like a movie or documentary of which you are the director.

Part 2

1. Now, sit comfortably and get into the habit-busting state*.

2. Imagine you are sitting in the cinema and about to start watching a film in which you are starring. It is a film about those five experiences all put together.

3. Watch the film on a big screen in front of you slowly from beginning to end, taking particular note of how you perform in the starring role.

4. Make what you are looking at bigger by doubling the size of the screen, and give the movie house surround sound.

5. Notice how good it feels to watch yourself on this huge screen in full colour in those moments of achievement.

6. As it ends, let the movie start over again so that it never actually finishes, and each time it begins the quality of the colour and sound become better and better and the film is brighter, sharper and clearer.

7. Scrutinize each event and notice how it feels, looks and sounds to watch that you on the big screen.
8. Think about how well that you have done, how much energy that you have put into each of those experiences.
9. As the film starts again, the picture is even larger and the volume is even greater. Repeat this at least five times.
10. Now stop.
11. Take a few deep breaths and bring your attention back to wherever you are.

Now do a critique: what would you say were among the qualities of the person you were watching? Would you give this person an Oscar for their performance? If not, go back and do it again, even if you have to go overboard and make up some of the situations.

Once they have given an award-winning performance, answer the following questions:

What would you say about this person? What are their qualities?
Are they persevering, no matter what?
Are they determined and focused on what they want?
Are they dedicated to self-improvement?
Are they really positive and filled with self-belief?

Write down the qualities you attribute to them. Make what you have written into a really powerful statement, such as 'They are really positive,' 'They are very focused,' 'They can do anything,' 'They have got what it takes.'

Now I want you to get out of the director's chair and step into this Oscar-winning performance while repeating the statement. But instead of saying: 'They are really positive' say 'I am really positive,' so your statement becomes a personal affirmation.

1. Now get back into state*.
2. Instead of sitting in the director's chair, step inside to take the lead role in your film and feel what it is like to experience those events all over again.
3. See what you saw, listen out for what you heard, and feel what it was like to achieve success in each instance.
4. Each time you go over this amazing feature-length film, feel how good it is in each of those events.
5. Repeat your affirmation to yourself, for example, 'I am always in control.' Say it as though you mean it, feeling the words inside your body as though you were shouting them from the rooftops.
6. Make the movie more real each time – brighter, bolder, clearer, louder – and go through it at least five times. It must be as though it never ends; it is just a continuous movie.

7.   Then take a few deeper breaths before slowly bringing
     your attention back to where you are.

If you are not convinced that you deserve an Oscar for that performance, do the exercise again. You can have as many takes
as you like to perfect your performance and your realization that
you have the power to change.

Once you know you can, think:

What was it about you then that helped you to succeed?
Were you motivated?
Were you confident?
Did you believe you could achieve?

Repeat the sentence you chose for yourself as the film critic:
'I persevere no matter what' or 'I am determined and focused
on what I want'.

Say it aloud, with conviction, and mean it.

This is your affirmation. Repeat it to yourself at least 100
times a day, always like you mean it.

I would also like you to get into the habit of saying it to yourself whenever you feel your self-belief beginning to ebb, or
when you want to be particularly effective or just more positive
about your ability to achieve. It could be anything. Don't worry if

it feels silly at first or you don't really believe it. Repeat it enough and you will. The more you use it, the better you will become at using it.

What you are doing is drawing on the resources you already have which, in the past, helped you to achieve success. What you should have realized is that you are far more resourceful than you think.

Now that you have watched and starred in the movie a few times, how do you feel?

With that feeling, think of some of the challenges that lie ahead in your mission to quit smoking. Do they seem like problems to the person whose achievements you have relived? You should be able to contemplate and face the challenges ahead with considerably more ease than before you sat down to make that list.

Mini Challenge – Repeating Your Affirmation Out Loud
Write down your affirmation in colour on a few pieces of paper and stick them up in places where you will see them regularly each day. Whenever you see the affirmation, repeat it out loud to yourself a few times as though saying it from the top of a mountain or shouting it from the rooftops.

Life is a movie you see through your own unique eyes. It makes little difference what's happening out there. It's how you take it that counts.

DENIS WAITLEY, *THE WINNER'S EDGE*

Give an Award-winning Performance

Have you noticed that some actors are so good at playing a role that you forget they are acting at all? Many of the best spend huge amounts of time getting into a part, thinking about how the character would think, feel, act and move through the world. We know we are not born with habits; we practise them, just like an actor learning a new role. All that I am trying to do now is to teach you how to break that habit and play a different version of you.

I once worked with a doctor who smoked. He had smoked for many years and it had, in the past, helped him at times of stress and anxiety to cope with the huge number of sick people with whom he had to deal. He admitted, however, that the smoking no longer gave him the relief or enjoyment it once had, and he felt guilty about the sort of example he was setting his patients. When he came to see me I suggested he spend some time imagining and pretending that he had never actually smoked. I told him to assume the identity of who he was without the cigarettes. A month after he had given up I asked him if it had been hard. 'It is pointless asking me that,' he said. 'It is as if I never have.'

As we have already seen, simply imagining an event or experience has an effect on the body. Research on sportsmen and women using a biofeedback machine has shown that as they imagine themselves competing, their heart rate, blood pressure and body temperature rise, as if they were actually competing physically. As this is the case, the potential for using our own imaginations in this way is enormous.

Assuming the Identity of an Ex-smoker

Special Agent, your next challenge is to assume the identity of an ex-smoker, or even better someone who has never smoked. Remember how you starred in the movie of your own success in Assignment 10? Well, now you are going to step inside that role again, and this time you are going to see, hear and feel through the mind and body of someone who has never smoked. So if a friend were to offer you a cigarette, you would immediately say 'no, thank you', or if for any reason you were tempted to smoke, you could even laugh at yourself as the mere thought of it is ludicrous and stupid.

Remember, it's not opening night, and you don't have to get the part right immediately, but the more you practise being the person you would like to be, the sooner it will come about.

The following challenge is a very important one and it will play a crucial role in your success.

Assume the identity of who you are _without_ the cigarettes.

Challenge – Make a Movie of Your Future

How about that movie of your own success? We can make it into a blockbuster, with absolutely no expense spared. In the movie you have broken your smoking habit. You are strong and in control. Some people find this difficult, but remember you are making this up. It lets you use your imagination. And if you don't get it right first time, you have the budget to make changes.

1. Get a notebook and get into the habit-busting state*.
2. Think of five scenarios in the future in which you are totally free of your habit (for example, in social situations or when you are stressed), and write them down.
3. Imagine these five experiences as pictures or snapshots in front of you.
4. Take the first one and see it moving closer to you until it is big enough to fill a large screen.
5. Look at yourself in the future, free from your habit, confident, positive and in control. Watch yourself carefully.
6. Make the picture clearer, brighter and bolder.
7. After 30 seconds, push the image back and repeat this process with each of the other four pictures.
8. Now, one at a time, allow each picture to move towards you until it moves inside you. Step into it for 30 seconds, feeling what it is like in the future to be in control and taking on the new way of behaving.
9. Do this with each snapshot, stepping in and out for 30 seconds, making sure each time that you make the experiences clearer and more real to you.
10. Finally, when you have done this with all the experiences, bring them all together, and step into the entire event like it is an ongoing movie, with one future event following

another. When it ends just start it again, making it even better. Keep going over it several times.

11. When you watch the film see yourself clearly, as though the future has already passed and you are watching a video recording. It must be as though the achievement has already happened, and there is nothing you can do about it. Your mind will then know the direction in which you want to go.

Doing this exercise once is rarely enough. You would not expect an actor to read a script through once to really get into the part. Go over and over it until you convince yourself you are that future you. Make it so that when it comes to imagining these events, you feel as though you are already there. You can, if you think you can.

Mini Challenge – Everyday Heroes

Is there someone you have watched undergo a remarkable change? I have watched 60-a-day smokers stop for good. I have seen them become healthier and happier, and more in control of their lives. If you know or ever meet anyone who tells or demonstrates a life-changing transformation, why not ask them how they did it? Their formula may not work the same wonders for you, but it would be worth a try.

Nobody gets to live life backwards. Look ahead, that is where your future lies.

ANN LANDERS

Consider the Cost ...

Main brand cigarettes in the UK now cost £4.40 (after the April 2002 budget).
The table below shows how much smoking costs at current prices.

Cigarettes per day	Years of smoking				
	1	5	10	20	50
5	£402	£2,008	£4,015	£8,030	£20,075
10	£803	£4,015	£8,030	£16,060	£40,150
20	£1,606	£8,030	£16,060	£32,120	£80,300
40	£3,212	£16,060	£32,120	£64,240	£160,600

Do you really want to waste that amount of money on a habit that could eventually kill you?

Stay on Track

Pleasure vs Pain

You may now be in the position of feeling very motivated about your choice to stop smoking. You have realized through the assignments you have completed so far that you have had enough of carrying around this unwanted habit like a millstone round your neck. You are taking many positive steps towards becoming a non-smoker. However, where each of us can come unstuck in our attempt to stop smoking is in failing to think beyond the immediate pleasure if we are in a situation where we may be tempted to smoke. For example, say you have stopped smoking for a time and you meet a friend who offers you a cigarette. You could make a picture of the immediate after-effects of indulging your habit, decide the effect will not be so dire, and then indulge. You can, however, learn to think about what is beyond the immediate picture, idea or impression.

Stop and think about that one cigarette and do the following challenge to see what the effects of it might be:

Challenge – See into Yourself

This is a practical challenge which will show you visually the real effects of smoking just one cigarette.

Get together the following:

- a cigarette
- a lighter
- a clear plastic bottle
- 6 cotton wool balls
- a pencil
- modelling clay or putty

1. Drop the cotton wool balls into the plastic bottle.
2. Mould the modelling clay into a ball shape and block the mouth of the bottle with it.
3. Use a pencil to poke a hole through the modelling clay until you see the pencil tip inside the bottle; then remove the pencil.

4. Stick one end of the cigarette (the filtered end, if you are using a filtered cigarette) into the hole created in the modelling clay. Light the cigarette.
5. Now gently squeeze the plastic bottle to simulate breathing. Squeezing the bottle draws cigarette smoke inside the bottle in the same way lungs draw smoke into the body.
6. After pumping the bottle a dozen times or so, extinguish the cigarette. Then remove the clay plug.
7. Look at the cotton wool balls in the bottom of the container.

You can now realize the impact of just one cigarette if you choose to continue indulging in your habit. Maybe you will only smoke one cigarette today, but over the weekend in the pub you could smoke ten, and before you know it you could be back where you started.

If you are tempted to smoke, stop, take a couple of deep breaths and think beyond the short-term pleasure to the long-term pain.

Mastering Failure

It is important for you to realize that failing is part of succeeding. For example, what do you think was the most natural thing you've ever had to learn? It was probably learning how to walk. Getting it right is an act of perpetually falling over, yet when we learned to do this, we were not conscious of continual failure. We simply got back on our feet and tried again, and again and again, until we could walk. At no point does a baby, because he or she keeps falling, think, 'Oh well, I may as well give up.' The natural and inherent desire to succeed is so strong that it compels the baby to keep on trying.

As we grow up, however, we tend to give ourselves such a hard time when we fail at something, that we fear ever trying again. But often, that is the only way to learn.

Anyone who has experienced success knows how to master failure. It is important to remember that those times of weakness when you slip back into your smoking habit are mishaps, not crises.

If, after each lapse when you break your habit, you can go over the situation and remember yourself not making the lapse, the chances are that, when faced with a similar set of circumstances, you won't make the mistake again. Your unconscious will start to follow the new roadmap of what you consciously want to do.

In fact, when you have a setback, laugh, especially if you don't feel like it. Doing that alone releases seratonin, which is what is known as the 'feeling of well-being' chemical. You cannot hold on to depressing or self-defeating thoughts when the corners of your mouth are up-turned. Try it – it is impossible. To keep your attitude to your progress – and any slip-ups that occur along the way – in proportion, smile. At this moment, instead of giving yourself a hard time, use it as an opportunity to refocus and take control.

Planning for Knock-backs

Preparing to fail sounds very negative, but you need to be armed with the ability to avoid temptation if you want to succeed in stopping smoking.

Plan to have knock-backs, because they do happen. How you deal with them will determine how successful you will be in breaking your habit. Think about and plan your reaction to potential setbacks along the way. Think about what it will be like to be offered a cigarette. How are you going to deal with this situation.

Rather than seeing stopping smoking as a problem, regard it as a personal challenge, and instead of focusing on or thinking so much about which part of the change is a problem, focus instead on the result of the change. What will you be like once you have achieved it? The change should feel much more attainable.

If there were no difficulties, there would be no triumphs.

Mini Challenge – Find the Strength to Say 'No'

You have tremendous power in the moment you say 'no' and mean it. Remember now the last time you said 'no' with real meaning and feeling. Recall now that feeling of really knowing, of being absolutely sure. Remember it again, in as much detail as you can, and hold on to that feeling. Practise, and you will be able to remember and harness that feeling whenever you are tempted to lapse back into your smoking habit.

A step in the wrong direction is better than staying on the spot all your life. Once you're moving forward you can correct your course as you go. Your automatic guidance system cannot guide you when you're standing still.

MAXWELL MALTZ

Boost Your Confidence and Self-Control

Some people find it easier than others to stop smoking, while a number achieve success fairly fast. None of this matters – getting there is all that counts.

I find that many people need their confidence building when they are trying to stop smoking. Those almost inevitable times of weakness that people experience can make them feel vulnerable, and as a result they can lapse back into their old ways. This is when they need to put themselves into a resourceful state, and rise above temptation.

Here are a couple of quick and easy techniques that you can turn to when you feel the need for extra confidence or self-control in your mission to stop smoking.

Re-centring Your Balance (Hara)

When asked, a friend of mine said the best thing about practising martial arts was the ability and confidence it gave him to say 'no'. It gave him control of himself and the state he was in, to the point where he could not be swayed by any outside influence. In practising this discipline, he was able to go into this state whenever he wanted or needed to.

Many practised martial artists are able to go into whichever state they want whenever they want. I once saw a show given by some martial artist monks who were demonstrating strength and flexibility by lying on beds of nails and doing somersaults in the air. These are people who have learned how to put their attention into the strongest part in their body: their centre.

Imagine you have a small tennis-size ball in the middle of your stomach, the strongest point in your body. Breathe into that part of your body and feel strong.

Whom do you know or admire who can stay in a resourceful state no matter what? When we are in a negative state of mind, we talk down to ourselves and our attention is all in our head. When we feel good, confident and strong, our attention is more evenly spread throughout our body and tends to concentrate in our centre, our stomach, making us feel much more balanced.

Could you imagine the golfer Tiger Woods or the former South African President Nelson Mandela talking to themselves negatively or giving themselves a hard time when under pressure?

Get a friend to stand by you for this next exercise.

1. Stand straight up with your eyes on the horizon and your feet shoulder-width apart.
2. Now think of a time when you've felt overwhelmed or stressed, perhaps at the amount of work in front of you, or at a task you've had to complete by a particular time.
3. You no doubt felt anxious and concerned about how you were going to get through this time.
4. As you concentrate on this feeling of anxiety and stress, tell your friend to push against your upper arm just below the shoulder in an attempt to force you over.
5. You should find that you are unable to put up much resistance: your brain is too focused on your problems to divert any strength to keeping you upright.
6. Now, find the point on your lower stomach that is about three finger-width spaces below your belly button. Those who practise yoga call this *hara*. Press a finger on that point and, as you take your finger away, relax completely and put your attention on that point.

7. Get your friend to try to push you over again. You should find that, this time, you are much more solid.

We spend much of our time with our attention fixed in our heads, worrying mostly, and wonder why we often feel wobbly and out of control.

When you need to feel more stable or in control, or the next time you are confronted by someone putting pressure on you to revert to your old habits, just switch your focus from your mind to that point below your naval. Your ability to face whatever difficulty you confront will automatically increase.

Creating Your Own Anchors

A smell, a tone of voice or a piece of music are examples of things that can remind us of people, places or feelings we've had in the past. They are known as *anchors*, because they anchor us to particular events in the past. There are also anchors that can remind us of times when we performed exceptionally well or when we felt particularly able or confident.

We can create our own anchors, so that when we feel the need for extra confidence or self-control, there is a means by which we can immediately tap into it.

1. Get into state*.
2. Remember a time when you performed exceptionally.
3. Imagine the experience as though you were there now.
4. You may find it easier to concentrate on one aspect of the memory at a time.
5. The more senses you use (see it, feel it, smell it, and so on), the easier it will become to recall and relive.
6. Once you have a strong representation of the memory, mark the experience in some way (such as pressing your hands together, rubbing your eyebrow, looking at your watch or saying a phrase to yourself) so your unconscious mind knows what you want it to do when you repeat this 'mark'.
7. You need to repeat marking the memory with the action again and again until you know, just by looking at your watch or pressing your hands together, that the mark and feeling are anchored.

Mini Challenge – Control the Urge!

Wear a rubber band on your wrist. When you have an urge to smoke, snap the rubber band and quietly say to yourself, 'No, stop!' Breathe in deeply as you say this, 1-2-3-4, and breathe out slowly.

Do this every time you have a craving to smoke. The more you do this, the more you will be able to control the urges, and the longer you will be able to go without a craving. Eventually you will be able to get rid of the rubber band and simply say to your urges, 'No, stop!'

The more you depend on forces outside yourself, the more they dominate you.

HAROLD SHERMAN

Take Care of Yourself

Success in breaking a habit does not last if you don't start to focus your attention on doing other things for yourself and taking on new life-affirming habits.

The habit of a lifetime, for most of us, should be taking better care of ourselves. But the majority of people, for a number of different reasons, do not know how to do this as effectively as they could.

Mainly it is because of the ways in which we have been conditioned as we have grown up. Many people think that they have to struggle, that there is something wrong with them, and that they are not good enough the way they are. These feelings along with the stresses and strains of life make some turn to external things to help them change the way they feel, such as smoking, drinking, drug taking or eating too much.

The problem comes when some of these habits are done to excess, as they can be dangerous and destructive. Unfortunately, this isn't going to apply to smoking – smoking is dangerous and destructive whether you smoke heavily or not because of the serious health risk that *every* cigarette poses to you.

Special Agent, your last assignment in your mission is to start taking better care of yourself. What follows are some simple techniques designed to help you feel good about yourself and your life.

Take on board the habit of a lifetime – the habit of truly taking care of yourself.

Be Successful at Being Happy

What does being successful mean to you? When asked, a great many people will define success as being when they have achieved something or reached a particular goal. I think this is strange, because I believe that all the times in between count as well. You are being successful even on the way to achieving a goal. Start being successful at being happy, and notice your success by how happy you are.

One of the secrets to doing this successfully is to love what you do and do what you love. I know this is not always easy, especially if you are in a job that you don't like or in a difficult relationship. But make a decision to enjoy what you do now, in the present, because that is what it is, a present, and it won't come round again. You are making your future now, so make the most of it.

By accepting this challenge you will learn how to take each moment as it comes, and this is the most effective tool in breaking habits.

Slow Down and Enjoy Each Moment

A friend of mine, who used to be a smoker, was telling me how annoyed he used to get with the graphic designers he was working with, because if they got stuck on something they would stop, sit back in their chair and light up a cigarette, and in time their inspiration would come to them.

However, it wasn't the cigarette that gave them inspiration, it was the fact that they had taken some time out and had some space to think about the solution.

I showed my friend how to achieve the same result without smoking – by taking a break, slowing down, going for a walk.

He took my advice and has become much more effective in dealing with problems when they arise.

If you smoke because you think it is helping you to deal with stress then part of your mission is to learn how to deal with your stress in some way other than smoking.

We seem to live life at an incredibly high speed, trying to cram all that we believe we need to do into a day. This is despite using any number of devices to help us save time and get on with what needs to be done. What do people really do with the time they save? No time is saved, really; it just tends to get filled up with more 'doing'. There is still no time for stillness, for enjoying each moment.

Most of us need to spend some time learning how to deal with and enjoy each and every moment, as this is all that we have control over. As we saw in Assignment 1, the best thing to do in every moment, in every day, is to take long, deep breaths. Here is another exercise to help you breathe that little bit more deeply and effectively.

Mini Challenge – Breathe Like a Special Agent

1. Lie down comfortably on the floor.
2. Place a fairly heavy book on your stomach, making sure it is resting comfortably.
3. As you breathe in through your nose allow your stomach to inflate and feel the book rising.
4. As you breathe out, allow the book to sink towards your stomach.
5. Do this for as long as you feel comfortable.
6. See how deep your breathing can become, how much you can move the book, how relaxed you can be.
7. Count your breaths, if that helps you to focus more clearly on your breathing.
8. You can do this exercise for as long as you like. When you have finished, take the book off, stand up slowly, and begin to consciously put this deep breathing into practise.

Remember, Special Agents always breathe deeply when facing any adversity, whether it be stress, fear or anxiety.

It is important from time to time to slow down, to go away by yourself, and simply be.

EILEEN CADDY, *THE DAWN OF CHANGE*

Imagine a Better You

Imagine what it is going to be like once you are taking better care of yourself.

Grab your notebook and write down:

- What you would be doing
- What would be different about your life
- What you would be eating
- What kind of exercise you would be taking
- How often and in what way you would be relaxing
- What you would not be doing any more
- How you would be feeling.

See yourself behaving in these ways, as though you are already taking better care of yourself. You can then begin to live the dream. It really is no more difficult than that. Achieve little bits at a time, for as long as it takes. You can win in every step you take towards being kinder to yourself – and don't let anyone else, for whatever reason, pull you away from your purpose.

Be Grateful For What You Have

A wealthy man decided one day to take his son to the home of a poor family so he could see how they lived. After spending a day and night in the farmhouse of this impoverished family, the man asked his son what he had learned. 'I saw that we have one dog and they have four. We have a pool in the garden and they have a creek with no end. I saw that we have imported lamps in the yard while they have the stars, and while our patio covers an acre they have the whole horizon. Thanks dad, for showing me how poor we are.'

Start being aware of what you do have in life, and focus on the things you can be grateful for, for example, a home, healthy children, a job, friends and family. Like passion and love, gratitude is a powerful emotion. Think about a time when you were really grateful for something. Would you agree that it is a feeling that fills you up? Be grateful for each day. See it as a gift.

Gratitude unlocks the fullness of life. It turns what we have into enough, and more.

MELODY BEATTIE

Enjoy Your New Life!

Congratulations on completing your mission. If it's **MISSION ACCOMPLISHED**, well done! If not, don't worry – you can start again at any time. The key to success is to stay positive and be patient with yourself and *not* to give yourself a hard time.

I once met a famous football player who had battled with various addictions. He overcame his adversity and really turned his life around. He told me that for him football is like life. He explained: 'It's not a question of falling down, because you always do; you trip, you make a tackle or you are knocked over. The real challenge is what you do when you get up. Some players learn from what happens and move on, and others carry it with them like a heavy burden.'

Life is not always the way it is supposed to be, it is the way it is. Adversity and struggle are an integral part of life, and how we deal with it will make the difference between staying behind and getting ahead.

When you get 'knocked over' or bad things happen to you, or you are 'triggered' to go back to your old ways, remember that you possess the power and capabilities to turn everything around. This is when you are being challenged and your resolve will be tested. Seize the moment and take control.

Good luck and take care of yourself, because you deserve it!

Further Help

Pete runs Habit Busting *Smoking* workshops, and he also sees individual clients who are ready to bust their smoking habit.

For more information, please visit Pete at:

www.Habitbusting.com

or email at:

info@Habitbusting.com

You can also write to Pete at:

Habit Busting
PO Box 2837
Leamington Spa
CV31 1WT

Tel: 0845 602 1607

Habit Busting

A 10-Step Plan That Will Change Your Life
Pete Cohen, With Sten Cummins

Simple Techniques to Stop Self-Sabotage, Break Bad Habits, and Achieve Your Potential

How would you like to be your best self all the time? To be free and successful at work? To eat healthily? To give up smoking? To stop procrastinating? According to the authors of *Habit Busting* it can be simple, it can be quick, and it can be fun.

In this invaluable guide Pete Cohen and Sten Cummins offer techniques to stop sabotaging yourself and straightforward strategies for bringing out your best. They will help you work with your strengths, learn from masters in whatever it is you want to accomplish and take stock of past behaviour – both what has worked for you and what hasn't. *Habit Busting* shows how, in just 21 days, you can turn a bad habit into a healthy one.

ISBN 0722540094

Fear Busting

A 10-Step Plan That Will Change Your Life
Pete Cohen

Following the success of his best-selling book *Habit Busting*, GMTV life coach Pete Cohen explains how to tackle the fears that prevent us from living the life we want, focussing on the fear of change.

⊘ Do you worry about making mistakes?
⊘ Are you afraid to try in case you get it wrong?
⊘ Is the fear of change making you make do with the life you have, when you know it could be so much better?

It doesn't have to be this way. In *Fear Busting*, Pete Cohen outlines simple strategies for tackling the fears that hold you back – especially the fear of change itself. By following Pete's motivational plan, you can change the way you see your life, so that challenges become chances, threats become opportunities and no obstacle is insurmountable.

ISBN 0 00 715109 8

Make
www.thorsonselement.com
your online sanctuary

Get online information, inspiration and guidance to help you on the path to physical and spiritual well-being. Drawing on the integrity and vision of our authors and titles, and with health advice, articles, astrology, tarot, a meditation zone, author interviews and events listings, www.thorsonselement.com is a great alternative to help create space and peace in our lives.

So if you've always wondered about practising yoga, following an allergy-free diet, using the tarot or getting a life coach, we can point you in the right direction.